Word Problems
Practice Book

Essential Learning Products Company, ©1995
P.O. Box 2590, Columbus, Ohio 43216-2590

Printed in the United States of America

ESSENTIAL
LEARNING
PRODUCTS

Guided Practice Workbook Series

Geography

Grammar

Handwriting

Math-Basic Operations

Math-Intermediate

Math-Word Problems

Phonics

Reading Comprehension

Reading

Social Skills

Spelling

Study Skills

Thinking Skills

Writing

Introduction

Many students who have mastered fundamental arithmetic skills have difficulty with word problems. The source of the difficulty is that they have not had enough practice. They know how to add, subtract, multiply, and divide, but when faced with a word problem, just do not know when to perform each operation.

This book is designed to help these students by providing extensive practice in solving word problems. Basic arithmetic involving whole numbers, fractions, money, and percentages make up the majority of the problems. Time, graphs, and maps are dealt with in the final portion of the book. Answers are provided in the back of the book. Wherever forms of measurement are involved, problems have been provided in both metric measure and in United States Customary measure. These pages may be handled according to the system used in the child's school.

It is important to note that this is a practice book, and that instruction must precede its use. At the beginning of each section there is an example of how to do that specific type of word problem, but the basic skills and concepts involved in the problems should have previously been acquired.

The word problems in each unit become progressively more challenging. The first problem is the easiest and the last is the most difficult. The units themselves, however, are not ordered according to difficulty. For this reason it is not necessary to begin with the first page and progress sequentially through the book.

Not everyone using this practice book will need to do all of the units. The book may be used to reinforce knowledge in a specific area, or to provide practice which will make previous instruction more understandable. It may also serve as a review to assure that concepts and practices in arithmetic word problems are thoroughly mastered.

Word Problems
Contents

Judy saves stamps. She put 76 in a book, and has 14 in a drawer. How many does she have altogether?

Answer __90__

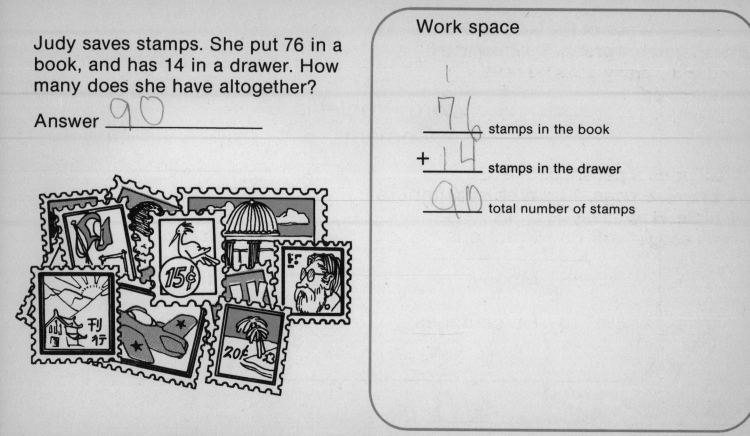

Work space

```
    1
   76
 + 14
 ————
   90
```

76 — stamps in the book
+14 — stamps in the drawer
90 — total number of stamps

Juan has a box of Pic Up Stix. He has 1 black, 4 green, 8 yellow and 6 red. How many does he have altogether? _____19_____

Pam owns a pet shop. She has 4 kittens, 6 dogs, 7 goldfish and 1 turtle. How many pets does she have altogether? _____18_____

$$
\begin{array}{r}
1 \text{ black} \\
+ 4 \text{ green} \\
+ 8 \text{ yellow} \\
+ 6 \text{ red} \\
\hline
19 \leftarrow \text{total}
\end{array}
$$

$$
\begin{array}{r}
1 \\
+ 4 \\
+ 6 \\
+ 7 \\
\hline
18 \leftarrow
\end{array}
$$

Benny sold pencils for his choir. He sold 4 to Mrs. Small, 2 to Mrs. Rite, 6 to Mr. Peters, and 1 to his mother.

How many pencils did he sell?

_____13_____

How many people bought pencils?

_____4 people_____

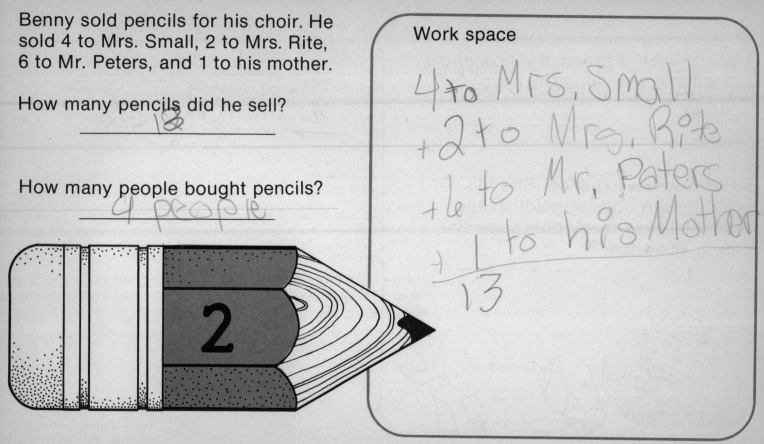

Work space

4 to Mrs. Small
+2 to Mrs. Rite
+6 to Mr. Peters
+1 to his Mother
+1
———
13

6

In your class, 16 children ride the bus to school, 13 children walk, and 6 ride in cars.

35

How many children are in your class altogether? _____

Work space

1
16
+ 13
+ 6
———
35

The school auditorium seats 1500 people. On the stage, 50 more can sit, and 70 can stand in the rear. How many people can be in the auditorium at one time?

At a recent convention here, 1100 people came from out of town, 75 came from other countries, and 28 live right here. How many people attended the convention altogether?

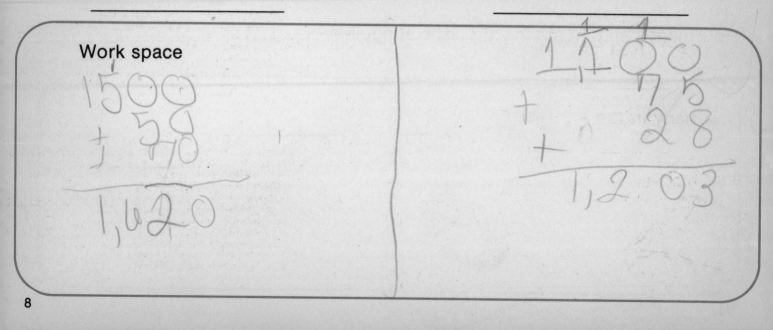

Work space

1500
+ 50
+ 70
—————
1,620

1100
75
+ 28
—————
1,203

Julie went to the zoo on Friday. In the morning, she saw 7 lions, 3 tigers, 4 bears, and 1 monkey. In the afternoon, she saw 1 horse, 6 deer, and 2 ducks.

How many animals did she see in the morning? (Just add them up!)

_____15_____

How many in the afternoon?

_____9_____

How many all day?_____24_____

Work space

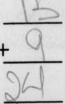

number in the morning	15
number in the afternoon	+ 9
number all day	24

In July, Harry painted 6 cabins, 4 cottages and 10 houses.
In August he painted 14 cabins and 12 cottages. In September he painted 8 houses, 2 cabins, and 1 cottage.

How many buildings did he paint in

September? ___11___

In July? ___20___

In August? ___26___

How many buildings did he paint in July and August together?

___46___

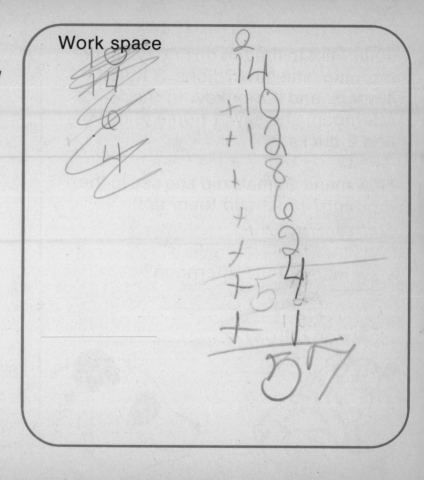

Work space

10

While on vacation at the shore, Mary and Lisa collected shells. The first day they found 20 shells. The second day they found 4 shells more than the first day, and the third day 2 more than the first day. How many shells did they collect?

Step 1.   Find out how many shells they collected each day.

Step 2.   Add up the number of shells collected each day.

Answer ___66___

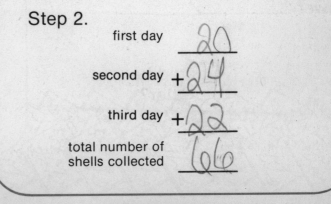

Work space

Step 1.

first day ___20___

second day = 24

third day = 22

Step 2.

first day ___20___

second day + 24

third day + 22

total number of shells collected ___66___

Junior had 20 comics and Alfred had 17. How many more comics did Junior have?

Answer _____ 13 _____

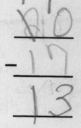

Junior's comics $\begin{array}{r} 1 \\ 2\overset{1}{0} \\ -17 \\ \hline 13 \end{array}$

Alfred's comics

Junior had this many more

Cathy and Joann had a party. Cathy invited 13 friends and Joann invited 19 friends.
How many more friends did Joann invite? _____32_____

My brother has 26 plants in his garden. I only have 14 plants in my garden. How many more plants does my brother have? _____12_____

Work space

$$\begin{array}{r} 19 \\ +13 \\ \hline 32 \end{array}$$

$$\begin{array}{r} 26 \\ -14 \\ \hline 12 \end{array}$$

Nancy read 26 pages in her book this week. Last week she read 38 pages. How many more pages did she read last week?

_____12_____

Sal is 12 and his mother is 37. What is the difference in their ages?

_____25_____

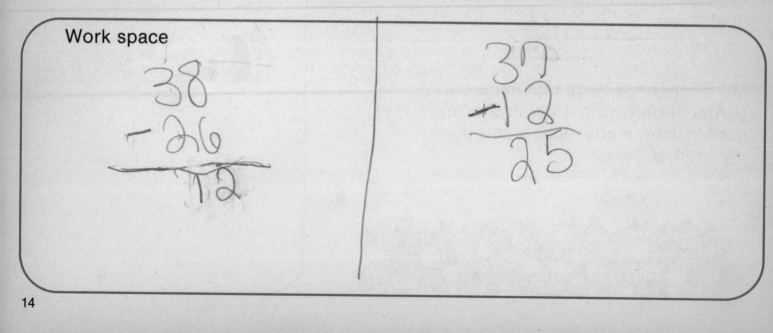

Work space

$$\begin{array}{r} 38 \\ -\ 26 \\ \hline 12 \end{array}$$

$$\begin{array}{r} 37 \\ +\ 12 \\ \hline 25 \end{array}$$

Restaurant

There were 35 people in the restaurant this morning and 64 people this afternoon. How many more people were in the restaurant this afternoon? _____ 29

A+

Work space

$$\begin{array}{r} 5 \\ 6\cancel{6}14 \\ -35 \\ \hline 29 \end{array}$$

Terry and Joe collect coins. Joe has 87 coins and Terry has 65. How many more coins does Joe have?

___22___

X

A

Terry has one coin dated 1906. Joe's oldest coin is dated 1927. How much older is Terry's coin?

___21___

Work space

$$\begin{array}{r} 87 \\ -65 \\ \hline 22 \end{array}$$

$$\begin{array}{r} 1906 \\ 1927 \\ -1906 \\ \hline 0021 \end{array}$$

Kathy has 100 apples and 63 pears to sell. How many more apples does she have?

_____37_____ A^+

The baseball season is 162 games and the football season is 16 games. How many more baseball games are there?

_____146_____

Work space

Marcy baked 48 raisin cookies and 31 oatmeal cookies. How many more raisin cookies did she bake?

_____17_____ A^t

Work space

$$\begin{array}{r} 48 \\ -31 \\ \hline 17 \end{array}$$

The first steam powered locomotive ran in 1829 and the first plane flew in 1903. How many years were there between these events?

_____74_____

$$\begin{array}{r} 1903 \\ -1829 \\ \hline 74 \end{array}$$

I drove 156 miles on my vacation. My sister drove 183 miles. How many more miles did my sister drive?

_____27_____

Ted drove 357 kilometers on his vacation. Barry drove 398 kilometers. How many more kilometers did Barry drive?

_____41_____

Work space

$$\begin{array}{r} 7 1\\ 18\cancel{3}\\ -156\\ \hline 27 \end{array}$$

$$\begin{array}{r} 398\\ -35\cancel{7}\\ \hline 41 \end{array}$$

19

There are 36 books on each shelf in a
library. If there are 8 shelves, how
many books are in the library?

Answer _____

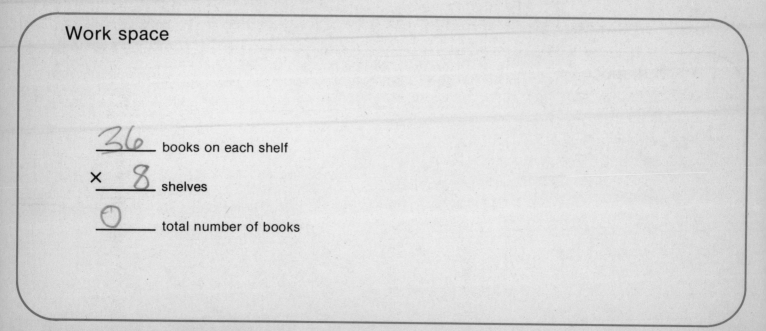

Work space

_36_ books on each shelf

× _8_ shelves

_0_ total number of books

If you have 7 bottles of juice and each bottle has 48 ounces in it, how many ounces do you have altogether?

_____ 55 _____

If you have 4 cartons of milk, and each carton has 250 milliliters in it, how many milliliters do you have altogether?

_____

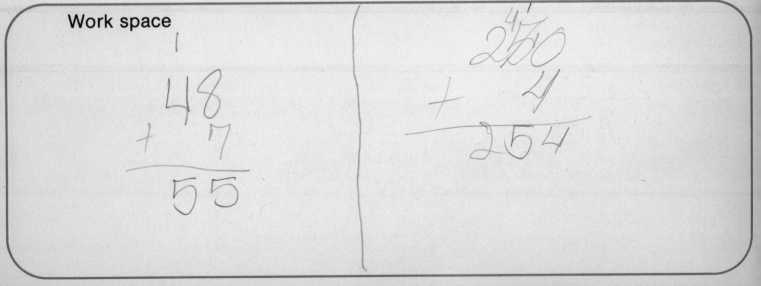

Work space

$$\begin{array}{r} 1 \\ 48 \\ + 7 \\ \hline 55 \end{array}$$

$$\begin{array}{r} 250 \\ + 4 \\ \hline 254 \end{array}$$

Each child in a class has 12 pieces of paper. If there were 15 children in the class, how much paper did they have altogether?

_____

If there were 23 children in the class, how much paper would they have?

_____

Work space

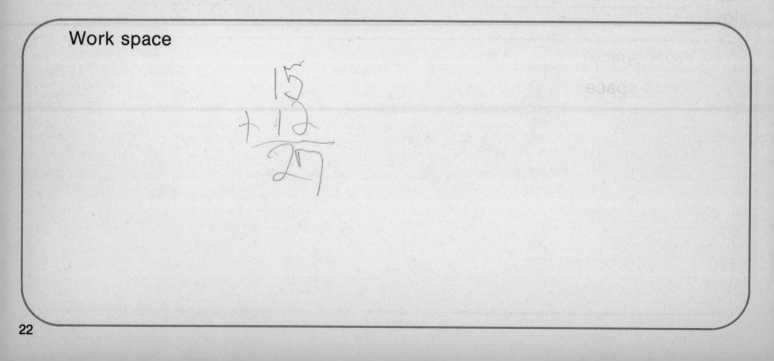

If a car goes 24 miles on a gallon of gas, how far could it go with 8 gallons? _____

If a truck goes 6 kilometers on a liter of gas, how far could it go with 40 liters? _____

Suppose you had 12 gallons of gas. How far could you go?

_____

Suppose you had 70 liters of gas. How far could you go?

_____

Work space

Sarah ran 4 kilometers in one week. How many meters did she run? (1 kilometer = 1000 meters)

_____

Ben used 6 yards of rope to build a swing. How many feet of rope did he use? (1 yard = 3 feet)

_____

If there are 4 weeks in a month, how many meters would Sarah run in a month?

_____

If Ben built 5 swings for a playground, how many feet of rope would he use?

_____

Work space

Ellen can plant 4 rows of vegetables with 1 package of seeds. How many rows of vegetables would she have if she planted 8 packages of seeds?

_____

If 20 plants grow in each row, how many vegetable plants would Ellen have altogether?

_____

Sam built 27 houses. Each house needed 12 windows. How many windows were needed altogether?

_____

There were 4 pieces of glass for each window. How much glass did Sam need?

_____

Work space

West builds tables. If he builds 15 tables each week, how many will he build in one year? (There are 52 weeks in a year.)

_____

How many chairs would he build if he made 7 each week for one year?

_____

Mr. Bray's classroom had 35 desks in 7 rows. The same number of desks were in each row. How many desks were in each row?

Answer _____

Work space

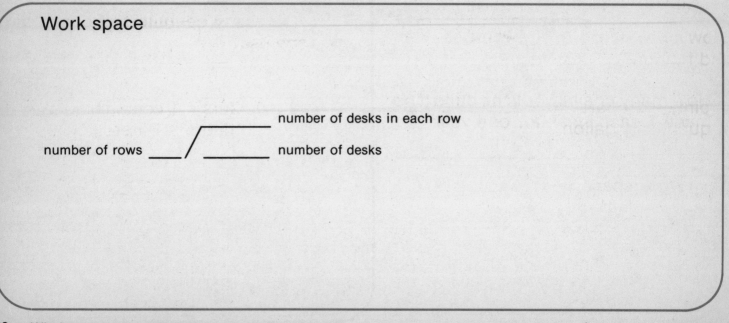

number of desks in each row

number of rows _____ /_____ number of desks

Lon bought 16 quarts of yogurt
and 16 pints of strawberries.
How many gallons
of yogurt did he buy?

_____

How many quarts of strawberries
did he buy?

_____

2 pints = 1 quart
4 quarts = 1 gallon

Betsy used 80 milliliters of cocoa
and 200 centiliters of milk in a
recipe. How many liters of milk did
she use?

_____

How many centiliters of cocoa did
she use?

_____

10 milliliters = 1 centiliter
100 centiliters = 1 liter

Work space

Tommie's class colored 140 Easter eggs. Each student got 5 eggs. How many students were in the class?

_____

The students in Tommie's class sat in 4 equal rows. How many students sat in each row?

_____

Work space

Susan works in a gas station. She used 592 quarts of oil. Each car she worked on needed 4 quarts of oil. How many cars did she work on?

Andy washed cars one weekend. He used a total of 405 liters of water to wash 9 cars. How many liters did Andy use on each car?

_____   _____

Work space

Gary had to drive from Washington, D.C. to Roanoke, Virginia, a distance of 360 kilometers. His car gets 12 kilometers per liter. How many liters would he need?

_____

John's motorcycle gets 30 miles to a gallon. He wanted to ride it 600 miles. How many gallons would he need?

_____

Work space

Ryan delivered newspapers. He delivered 285 papers to 15 people. Each person got the same number of papers. How many did each person get?

_____

Ryan's sister also delivered newspapers. She had the same number of people as her brother but delivered 255 papers. How many did each person get?

_____

Work space

In a big city, 1653 children have 29 different teachers. Each teacher has the same number of students. How many students does each teacher have?

_____

The children are in 3 schools. How many are in each school?

_____

Last year, there were 5044 rain storms in the United States. How many storms were there each week? (There are 52 weeks in a year.)

_____

How many were there in each season? (There are four seasons — summer, fall, winter, and spring.)

_____

Work space

On Monday Donna and Jim sent invitations to 36 people. By Thursday 24 people had called to say they could come and 8 people had called to say they could not come. How many had not called yet?

Step 1.   Find out how many people had called.

Step 2.   Subtract those who called from total number invited.

Answer _____

Work space

Step. 1.

_____ people who said yes

+ _____ people who said no

_____ total who had called

Step 2.

_____ total number invited

− _____ total who had called

_____ number who had not called

Laura sold 1600 pounds of fish. Smith's market bought 350 pounds, Miller's took 425 pounds, and the Corner Store bought 375 pounds. How many pounds did she have left to sell to Tom's Market?

_____

Peck's Orchard was shipping out a total of 1200 kilograms of fresh fruit. There were 450 kilograms of oranges, 310 kilograms of grapefruit, and 260 kilograms of lemons. How many kilograms of limes were there?

_____

Work space

Tina had 35 colors of paint. In her picture of a barn she used 7 colors. In her picture of flowers and fruit she used 9 different colors.

How many colors did she use altogether?

_____

How many did she not use?

_____

Mrs. Lewis took a bus from Denver to Chicago. The bus went 217 kilometers the first afternoon and 724 kilometers during the night. It is 1604 kilometers from Denver to Chicago. How far did the bus still have to go?

_____

Mr. Adams drove a truck from New York to Florida. On the first day he drove 385 miles, the second day 363 miles. It is 1033 miles from New York to Florida. How far must he drive the third day?

_____

Work space

Some children picked up 1600 empty cans. They worked 3 hours on Friday and 5 hours on Saturday. How many cans did they pick up each hour?

Step 1. Find out how many hours they worked.

Step. 2.   Divide the number of cans picked up by the number of hours.

Answer _____

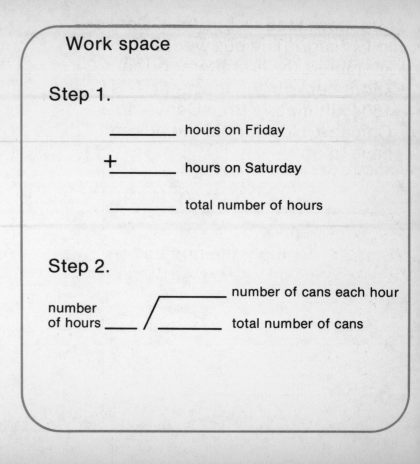

Work space

Step 1.

_____ hours on Friday

+_____ hours on Saturday

_____ total number of hours

Step 2.

number of hours _____ / _____ number of cans each hour
_____ total number of cans

Carolyn could read 4 pages every 2 minutes. At that rate, how many pages could she read in an hour? (60 minutes = 1 hour)

Step 1.   Find out how many pages she reads each minute.

Step 2.   Multiply the number of pages each minute by the number of minutes in an hour.

Answer _____

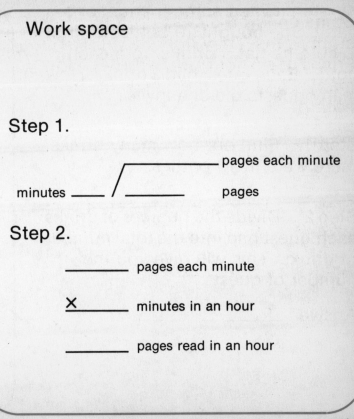

Work space

Step 1.

_____ pages each minute

minutes _____ / _____   pages

Step 2.

_____ pages each minute

× _____ minutes in an hour

_____ pages read in an hour

Kyrsten invited some friends for a party. She bought 10 bottles of fruit juice. She got 5 drinks from each bottle. Each guest had 2 drinks. How many guests did she invite?

Step 1.   Find out how many drinks there were in 10 bottles.

Step 2.   Divide the number of drinks each guest had into the total number of drinks. This will give you the number of guests.

Answer _____

Work space

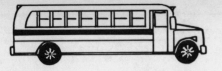

There were 1130 children on a trip. When it began to rain, 26 of them went home by car. The rest went home on 23 buses. The same number of children were on each bus. How many were on each bus?

Step 1.   Find out how many children went home by bus.

Step 2.   Divide the number of children who went home by bus by the number of buses. This will give you the number of children on each bus.

Answer _____

Work space

If you caught 45 fish in 3 days, how many fish would you catch in 12 days?

Step 1.   Find out how many fish you catch in one day.

Step 2.   Multiply the number of fish you catch in one day by the total number of days.

Answer _____

Work space

Reminder page: fractions

When you add or subtract fractions, the bottom number (the denominator) must be the same for all fractions.

$$\frac{1}{4} \qquad \frac{1}{4}$$
$$+\frac{1}{2} \longrightarrow +\frac{2}{4}$$
$$\frac{3}{4}$$

$$\frac{2}{3} \longrightarrow \frac{8}{12}$$
$$-\frac{1}{4} \longrightarrow -\frac{3}{12}$$
$$\frac{5}{12}$$

When you multiply fractions, you multiply across the top and across the bottom.

$$\frac{1}{2} \times \frac{1}{4} = \frac{1 \times 1}{2 \times 4} = \frac{1}{8}$$

When you divide fractions, you turn the number that divides upside down and multiply the number to be divided.

$$\frac{1}{2} \div 5 \longrightarrow \frac{1}{2} \times \frac{1}{5} \left(\left(\frac{5}{1}\right)\right) \longrightarrow \frac{1 \times 1}{2 \times 5} = \frac{1}{10}$$

When multiplying or dividing, cancel when you can. It makes the problem easier.

$$\frac{\overset{1}{\cancel{2}}}{5} \times \frac{3}{\underset{2}{\cancel{4}}} = \frac{3}{10} \qquad \frac{\overset{4}{\cancel{24}}}{3} \times \frac{1}{\underset{1}{\cancel{6}}} = \frac{4}{3} = 1\frac{1}{3}$$

When you have the answer, make sure it is in its simplest form.
Reduce fractions.

$$\frac{2}{4} = \frac{1}{2} \qquad \frac{8}{12} = \frac{2}{3}$$

Change improper fractions to mixed numbers.

$$\frac{5}{3} = 1\frac{2}{3} \qquad \frac{17}{4} = 4\frac{1}{4}$$

At breakfast Judy drank $\frac{1}{8}$ liter of orange juice, Bill drank $\frac{1}{8}$ liter, and Annie $\frac{3}{8}$ liter. How much orange juice did they drink?

_____

Sam drank $\frac{1}{2}$ pint of milk at lunch. Maria drank $\frac{1}{2}$ pint, and Rod $\frac{1}{2}$ pint. How many pints of milk did they drink?

_____

Work space

Sara needs to make curtains. She needs $5\frac{1}{2}$ yards of material, $15\frac{1}{2}$ yards of trim, and $5\frac{1}{2}$ yards of backing. How much fabric will she buy?

_____

Jack was wrapping presents. He used $2\frac{1}{4}$ meters of blue ribbon, $1\frac{1}{4}$ meters of white ribbon, and $2\frac{3}{4}$ meters of green ribbon. How many meters did he use altogether?

_____

Work space

For the picnic, Sonja bought $6\frac{3}{4}$ pounds of hot dogs and $10\frac{1}{2}$ pounds of hamburger. How much did the meat weigh altogether?

Step 1.   Make sure the bottom numbers (denominators) of the fractions are the same.

Step 2.   Add the whole numbers and add the fractions.

Step 3.   Reduce the fraction if possible and simplify the answer.

Answer _____

Step 1. $10\frac{1}{2} = 10\frac{2}{4}$

Step 2.

Step 3.

Sharon was making punch. She used $2\frac{1}{2}$ liters of orange juice, $1\frac{2}{3}$ liters of lemonade, and $\frac{3}{4}$ of a liter of pineapple juice. How many liters of juice did she use altogether?

Paul needed $\frac{1}{2}$ cup of raisins, $1\frac{1}{3}$ cups of nuts, and $\frac{1}{4}$ cup of chopped dates to make a snack. How many cups did he need altogether?

_____   _____

Work space

My cousin and I had $\frac{1}{5}$ of a jigsaw puzzle
put together on a table. We dropped $\frac{4}{5}$ of
the puzzle. After looking around, we found
$\frac{3}{5}$ of the puzzle. What fraction of the puzzle
was still lost?

Answer _____

Work space

_____ fraction of puzzle that was dropped

− _____ fraction of puzzle that was found

_____ fraction of puzzle still lost

Trini had 2 quarts of milk. His recipe took $\frac{3}{4}$ quart. How much milk would he have left?

Step 1. Borrow from the whole number to subtract the fraction. Remember that $1 = \frac{4}{4}$.

Step 2. Subtract.

Answer _____

Step 1. $2 = 1\frac{4}{4}$

Amy was working on a science experiment. She measured 5 milliliters of water into a dish. Later, she discovered that $1\frac{1}{4}$ milliliters had evaporated. How much water was left in the dish?

_____

Susan found an old pot covered with dirt. It weighed $\frac{5}{6}$ of a pound. After she cleaned it up, the pot weighed $\frac{2}{3}$ of a pound. How much dirt was on the pot?

_____

Work space

A large can of beans weighed $2\frac{1}{2}$ pounds. The can alone weighed $\frac{3}{8}$ of a pound. How many pounds of beans were in the can?

_____

A box of nails weighs $1\frac{3}{4}$ kilograms. The nails alone weigh $1\frac{1}{2}$ kilograms. How many kilograms does the box weigh?

_____

Work space

Stuart bought $30\frac{1}{2}$ kilograms of dog food for his dogs. After a month, he had $2\frac{1}{5}$ kilograms left. How many kilograms had his dogs eaten?

_____

Phil had $16\frac{2}{3}$ tons of coal. He burned $12\frac{1}{4}$ tons. How much coal did he have left?

_____

Work space

Peg had 9 apples. Rita had $\frac{1}{3}$ as many. How many did Rita have?

Step 1.   Multiply across the top and across the bottom.

Step 2.   Reduce the fraction if possible.

Answer _____

Step 1.

$$9 \times \frac{1}{3} = \frac{9}{1} \times \frac{1}{3} =$$

About $\frac{1}{2}$ of Nate's land is covered with trees, and about $\frac{1}{6}$ of the trees are pine. What fraction of Nate's land is covered with pine trees?

Answer _____

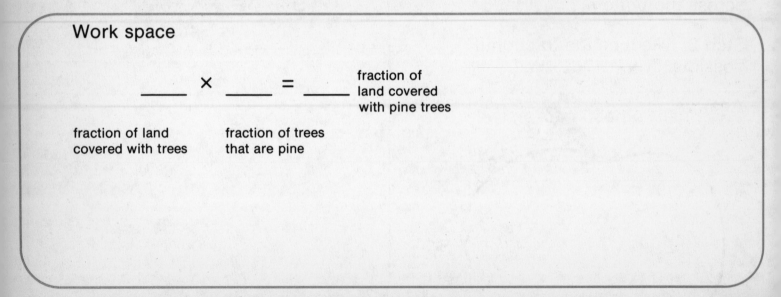

Work space

_____ × _____ = _____ fraction of land covered with pine trees

fraction of land covered with trees

fraction of trees that are pine

Ted said he was going to take $\frac{1}{5}$ of the books on the table. There were 45 books on the table. How many books would Ted take?

_____

There were 56 crackers on a plate and $\frac{1}{8}$ of them were wheat crackers. How many wheat crackers were there?

_____

Connie was moving. While packing, she found that one shelf of books took up $1\frac{1}{5}$ boxes. If she had 10 shelves to pack, how many boxes would she need?

Step 1.   Change the mixed fraction (whole number with a fraction) into an improper fraction (the top number is greater than the bottom number).

Step 1.

$$1\frac{1}{5} = \frac{6}{5}$$

Step 2.   Multiply. (Cancel if you can. The problem will be easier.)

Step 2.

Answer _____

Robert drove his boat across the river. It took $1\frac{1}{2}$ gallons of gas for one trip. If he crossed the river 24 times how much gas did he use?

_____

A laundromat uses $2\frac{2}{3}$ kiloliters of water in one month. How much water will it use over a period of one year (12 months)?

_____

Work space

You have $1\frac{1}{4}$ barrels of oil and you divide it into 5 pots. How much goes into each pot?

Step 1.   Change the mixed number into an improper fraction.

Step 2.   Turn the number that divides upside down and multiply the number to be divided.

Step 3. Reduce the answer if possible.

Answer _____

Work space

Step 1.

$$1\frac{1}{4} = \frac{5}{4}$$

Step 2.

$$\frac{5}{4} \div 5 \rightarrow \frac{5}{4} \times \frac{1}{5} =$$

Step 3.

A butcher divided $10\frac{1}{2}$ kilograms of meat into 7 packages. How many kilograms were in each package?

_____

Smitty had $12\frac{1}{2}$ bushels of peas. He divided them among his 5 friends. How many bushels did each friend get?

_____

Work space

You have $4\frac{4}{5}$ loaves of bread left from the bake sale. 6 people each want to take some home. How much does each person get?

_____

Louis made $8\frac{1}{3}$ bowls of spaghetti sauce. He wants to divide the amount evenly into 5 jars and freeze it. How much will go into each jar?

_____

Work space

Mike has $31\frac{1}{2}$ grams of salt to divide evenly into 9 shakers. How many grams will he put into each shaker?

_____

You have $4\frac{1}{2}$ pounds of beans, and want to put them into 3 baskets. Each basket has the same amount of beans. How many pounds of beans will be in each basket?

_____

Work space

You spent 2 hours on your home-work. History took 1/4 of the time and math took 1/3 of the time. The remainder of the time was spent on reading. How much time was spent on reading?

Step 1.   Find the common denominator and add the fractions of time spent on history and math.

Step 2.   Find out what the remaining fraction of your whole time was. This will tell you what fraction of the time was spent on reading.

Step 3.   Multiply the number of hours by the fraction of time spent on reading. This will tell you how many hours you spent on reading.

Answer _____

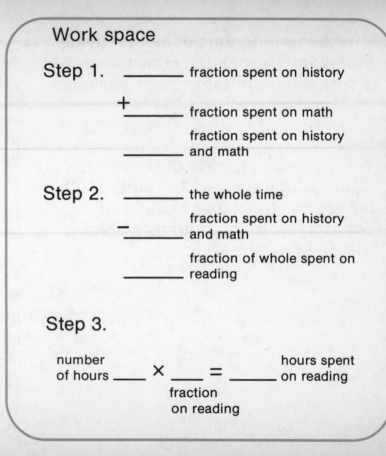

Work space

Step 1.   _____ fraction spent on history

+ _____ fraction spent on math

_____ fraction spent on history and math

Step 2.   _____ the whole time

− _____ fraction spent on history and math

_____ fraction of whole spent on reading

Step 3.

number of hours ____ × ____ = _____ hours spent on reading

fraction on reading

Julius went on vacation for 6 days. He spent $\frac{1}{2}$ of the time camping and $\frac{1}{4}$ of the time at the beach. The rest of the time he spent driving. How many days did he spend driving?

_____

Our library has 4150 books. $\frac{1}{5}$ of the books are written in French and $\frac{1}{10}$ are written in Spanish. The rest are written in English. How many books are written in English?

_____

Work space

Jerry's room was 150 square feet. The bed took up $\frac{1}{5}$ of the room and the other furniture took up $\frac{1}{2}$ the room. How many square feet were left to play in?

_____

Carol's garden was 42 square meters. She planted peppers in $\frac{1}{6}$ of the garden and cucumbers in $\frac{1}{3}$ of the garden. How many square meters were left for other plants?

_____

In a town of 2500 people, $\frac{1}{5}$ of the people work at a factory. The factory has 4 parts, each with the same number of people. How many people work in each part of the factory?

_____

Of the 1800 cookies baked in a bakery, $\frac{1}{6}$ are raisin cookies. If each raisin cookie has 9 raisins in it, how many raisins are used?

_____

Work space

Penny is driving from Houston to Dallas, a distance of 390 kilometers. She drives for $2\frac{1}{2}$ hours and covers $\frac{1}{2}$ of the distance. How many kilometers per hour did she drive?

_____

The distance from New York to Los Angeles is 3000 miles. Part of the distance, about $\frac{1}{4}$ of it, is through mountains. You can only drive 40 miles per hour through the mountains. How long will it take to go through the mountains?

_____

Work space

Reminder page: money

Money amounts can be written in several different ways:

7 dollars and fifteen cents = $7.15
 twenty-seven cents = 27¢ = $.27

When you work money problems, it is the same as using decimals.

```
 $2.48      $8.59      $ 2.50
+1.16      -6.12      ×    5
 $3.64      $2.47      $12.50
```

```
                    8.25
$24.75 ÷ 3 = 3/24.75
                    24
                    ‾7‾
                    _6_
                    15
```

At a restaurant, a hamburger cost $.89 and a glass of milk was $.45. How much would they be together?

Answer _____

Work space

$1.29
+ .65

Sally wanted to paint her bedroom. She needed 1 gallon of blue paint at $6.95, 1 quart of enamel at $3.95, and 1 quart of white ceiling paint for $3.75. How much did the paint cost?

_____

Ken bought 1 liter of juice for $1.59, 250 grams of cheese for $1.85, and a box of detergent for $3.37. How much did he spend?

_____

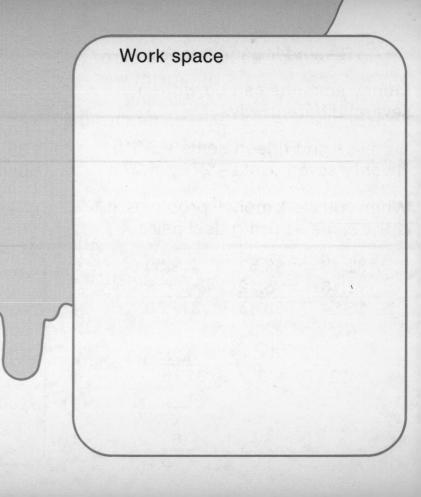

Work space

John's father was building a barn. Wood cost $420.00, and paint was $160.00. Nails cost $45.00, and windows were $65.00. How much did John's father spend on the barn?

_____

Art bought a new rug for $325.00 and a chair for $240.00. He also spent $115.00 on a coffee table and $80.00 on a lamp. How much money did he spend altogether?

_____

Work space

Marcy had $450.00 in the bank. She received $22.50 for her birthday, $25.00 for cutting lawns, and $16.50 for babysitting. How much did she have altogether?

_____

Sandy works in a department store. One day she sold a dress for $55.00, a blouse for $26.50, a coat for $150.00, and a sweater for $11.40. How much money did she have at the end of the day?

_____

Your allowance is $5.00 a week. If you spend $3.25 for school lunch, how much would you have left?

_____

If you went to the store with $10.00 and bought a game that cost $7.95, how much would you have left?

_____

Work space

To buy a bicycle, you need $69.85.
You have $52.15. How much more
money do you need?

_____

If you earn $25.00 for shoveling
snow, and you want to buy a sled that
costs $37.50, how much more money
do you need?

_____

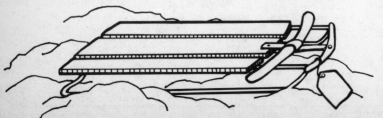

Work space

Each year your parents spend $180.00 to buy you clothes. They spend $43.00 on shoes. How much is left for other clothes? _____

Janet's paycheck is $186.00. She spends $58.60 on clothing and saves the rest. How much does she save? _____

Work space

A new car costs $14,875. You trade in your old car for $7,034.00. How much more money do you need for the new car? _____

Jack needed $6843.00 to remodel his house. If he had $5676.00 in the bank, how much more money did he need?

_____

An egg costs about $.07. How much would a dozen cost?

_____

Reflectors for a bicycle cost $.60 a piece. If Laurie buys 6 for her bicycle, how much will she spend?

_____

Work space

Lisa bought 15 plums for $.09 each. How much did she spend?

_____

You work 8 hours a day for $5.10 an hour. How much do you make each day?

_____

Vince sells 6 neckties for $9.50 each. How much money does he take in?

_____

Work space

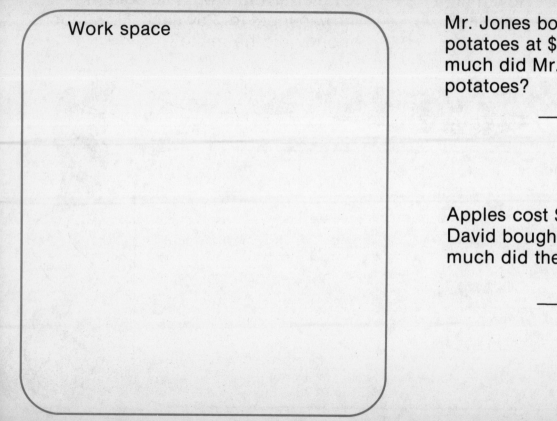

Work space

Mr. Jones bought 4 bushels of potatoes at $4.20 a bushel. How much did Mr. Jones pay for the potatoes?

_____

Apples cost $2.10 per kilogram. David bought 5 kilograms. How much did the apples cost him?

_____

Don bought 96 stamps. How much did he have to pay if stamps cost 34¢ each?

One afternoon, Mr. Hill sold 47 newspapers for 25¢ each. How much money did he make?

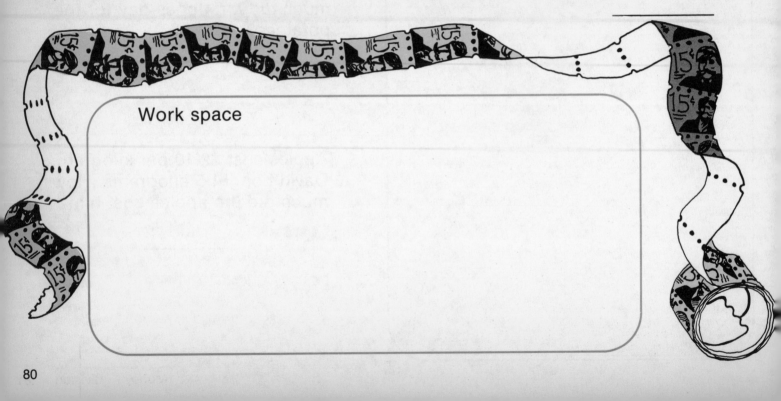

Work space

If sweaters were on sale at 3 for $45.00, what would 1 sweater cost?

_____

Melanie, Anita, and Pablo were rewarded $24.00 for returning a lost puppy to its owner. If they shared the reward equally, how much money did they each get?

_____

Work space

Mrs. McDowell spent a total of $2.10 for 6 spools of thread. How much did each spool cost?

_____

If 4 students saved a total of $96.00, how much had each one saved?

_____

3 painters painted a room and earned $165.00. How much did each painter receive?

_____

Work space

The senior class needed $150.00 for a class trip. There were 60 students in the class. How much would each have to earn?

_____

75 members of a club paid a total of $345.00 in dues. How much did each member pay?

_____

Work space

In September, the Andersons filled their heating oil tanks for the winter. Their tanks hold 1450 liters of oil and the bill was $319.00. How much did heating oil cost per liter?

_____

It cost us $92.56 to drive from San Francisco to Milwaukee. We used 89 gallons of gas. How much did gas cost us per gallon?

_____

Work space

June sells food. In the morning she started work with $175.00. She sold $785.50 worth of food, and paid $85.50 in bills. How much did she have at the end of the day?

Step 1.   Find out how much money June had before she paid the bills.

Step 2.   Subtract the amount June had to pay from how much she had.

Answer _____

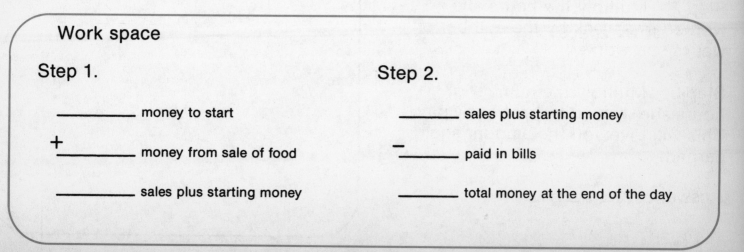

Work space

Step 1.

_____ money to start

+
_____ money from sale of food

_____ sales plus starting money

Step 2.

_____ sales plus starting money

−
_____ paid in bills

_____ total money at the end of the day

Pat was a teacher's aid. She worked 6 hours a day, 4 days a week. She worked 3 weeks. If she was paid $6.00 an hour, how much did she earn?

Step 1.   Find out how many hours she worked in one week.

Step 2.   Multiply the hours she worked in a week by the number of weeks she worked.

Step 3.   Multiply the number of hours she worked by her hourly pay. This will give you the amount she earned.

Answer _____

Work space

Ice cream is on sale for $1.80 for $\frac{1}{2}$ gallon. How much would 5 gallons of ice cream cost?

Step 1.   Find out how much one gallon of ice cream costs.

Step 2.   Multiply this number by the total number of gallons.

Answer _____

Apple cider costs $.68 a liter at a roadside stand. In a store it costs $.84 a liter. How much will you save if you buy 8 liters at the roadside stand?

Step 1.   Find the difference between the two prices.

Step 2.   Multiply the difference in price by the number of liters to be purchased.

Answer _____

Work space

An air conditioner costs 30¢ an hour to run. What would it cost to air condition a room 8 hours a day for 1 week? (7 days)

Step 1.   Find the cost per day for 8 hours of air conditioning.

Step 2.   Multiply the cost per day by the number of days.

Answer _____

If the air conditioner ran only 5 hours a day, what would the cost be for 1 week?

Step 1.   Find the cost per day for 5 hours of air conditioning.

Step 2.   Multiply the cost per day by the number of days.

Answer _____

What is the difference between the two costs? _____

Work space

Reminder page: percentages

The symbol for percent is %. It comes from the number 100.
When you have all of something, you have 100%.

When you add or subtract
percentages, you can keep the %
symbol and work the problem just
like it involved whole numbers.

$$\begin{array}{r} 30\% \\ +15\% \\ \hline 45\% \end{array} \qquad \begin{array}{r} 100\% \\ -\ 25\% \\ \hline 75\% \end{array}$$

When you multiply or divide using
percentages, it helps to change the
percentage to a decimal. For percentages
less than 10, you must remember to add a
zero when changing it to a decimal.

$25\% = .25$
$5\% = .05$
$.93 = 93\%$
$.08 = 8\%$

$160 \times 25\% \longrightarrow$

$$\begin{array}{r} 160 \\ \times\ .25 \\ \hline 800 \\ 320\ \ \\ \hline 40.00 \end{array}$$

When you want to find what percentage
one number is of another number, most
of the time you divide the smaller number
by the bigger number. The answer will be
a decimal which you must remember to
change to a percentage.

What percent of 40 is 10?

$$\frac{10}{40} = \ \ 40\overline{)10.00}^{\ .25} = 25\%$$

$$\begin{array}{r} \underline{8\ 0}\ \ \\ 2\ 00 \\ \underline{2\ 00} \end{array}$$

89

If Lisa sold 19% of the tickets to a football game and Francisco sold 32%, what percentage would they have sold together?

_____

If Skip painted 41% of a wall and Willy painted 13%, what percentage of the wall would they have painted?

_____

Work space

On Monday 10% of the class went to the library. On Tuesday 20% went, on Wednesday 35% went, and on Thursday 12% went. What percentage of the class had gone to the library, Monday through Thursday?

_____

For the play, Jim set up 26% of the chairs, Matt set up 19% and Eric set up 32%. What percentage of the chairs did they set up altogether?

_____

During the summer, 24% of the people in town went to the beach, and 57% went to the mountains. The rest of the people *didn't* take a vacation. What percentage of the people did take a vacation?

Answer _____

At the picnic, 43% of the people ate chicken, and 48% ate hot dogs. What percentage ate chicken or hot dogs?

_____

During free time, 26% of the class played a game and 44% went to the library. Some students, 17% of the class, went outside and 13% studied.

What percentage played a game or went to the library?

_____

What percentage studied or went outside? _____

Of the trees in a forest, 37% are fir trees, 23% are oak, 21% are spruce, and 19% are walnut.
What percentage are oak or walnut?

_____

What percentage are fir or spruce?

_____

Work space

When the school team played baseball, Frances got a hit 36% of the time and Michael got a hit 32% of the time. What is the difference in their hit percentage?

_____

Helen read 45% of her book and Andy read 67% of his book. What is the difference in the percentage they read?

_____

Work space

Tyrone got 86% on his test and Darcy got 98% on hers. What was the difference in their scores?

_____

Frank spends 55% of his free time in the gym and Ed spends 78% of his time in the gym. What is the difference in their percentages?

_____

Work space

Yesterday, we ate 45% of the peanuts in the jar. What percentage was left for today? (Remember, when you start out with *all* of something, like all the peanuts in the jar, that equals 100%.)

———

This morning, Karen washed 70% of the windows in her house. What percentage does she have to wash this afternoon to finish the job?

———

Sandy did 64% of the clean-up work. How much was left to do?

_____

Brian and his brother delivered newspapers. If Brian delivered 41% of the papers, what percentage was left for his brother to deliver?

_____

Work space

Last Saturday, 1500 people went to the football game. At half time, 15% of them bought hot dogs. How many people bought hot dogs?

Step 1.   Change 15% to a decimal.

Step 2.   Multiply the total number of people times the decimal.

Answer _____

Work space

"You are in class for 60 minutes and you pay attention 85% of the time," said the teacher. How many minutes was the class paying attention?

_____

Mr. and Mrs. King drove for 90 minutes. If Mr. King drove 70% of the time, how many minutes did he drive?

_____

Work space

At a restaurant, 52% of the people ate the chicken dinner. How many people ate chicken if 150 people went to the restaurant?

_____

On my parents' farm, 28% of the animals are cows. If my parents have 50 animals, how many are cows?

_____

Work space

We painted 3 rooms in our house and had 5 gallons of paint. We used 95% of the paint. How much did we use?

_____

If a water tank holds 90 liters and it is 80% full, how many liters are in the tank?

_____

Work space

Isabelle's class collected 90% of the cost of new sports equipment. There are 45 students in her class. If everyone collected the same amount, what percentage did each student collect?

Answer _____

Work space

number of students _____ / _____ percentage each student collected

percentage collected

A group of 5 friends pulled a sled 75% of the way up the hill. If each of them pulled the sled the same amount, what percentage of the way did each one pull the sled?

Answer _____

Work space

Work space	The sixth grade class has 25 students in it. The class did 75% of the decorations in the gym. If each student did the same amount, what percentage of the work did each student do?
	_____
	If 31 Girl Scouts earned 93% of the money needed for a field trip, what percentage did each Girl Scout earn?
	_____

There were 48 people at the party, and 24 of them brought presents. What percentage of the people brought presents?

Step 1.   Divide the number of people who brought presents by the number of people at the party.

Step 2.   Change answer from decimal form to a percentage.

Answer _____

Work space

Step 1.

Step 2.

number of people
at the party ____ / _____ number of people who brought presents

____ = ____ %

When you played basketball, you tried 30 shots and made 9. What percentage of your shots did you make?

The distance from Jack's house to the school is 16 blocks. If Jack rode his bike 4 blocks, what percentage of the distance did he ride?

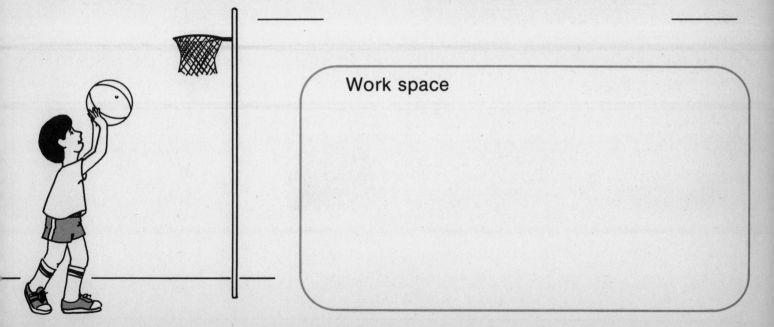

Work space

Only 4 students in a class of 40 had the flu. What percentage of the class was sick?

_____

Of the 125 people at the beach, 15 did not go swimming. What percentage did not go swimming?

_____

Work space

There are 52 weeks in a year. If summer is 13 weeks long, what percentage of the year is this?

_____

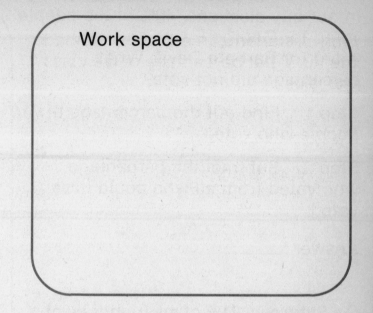

Work space

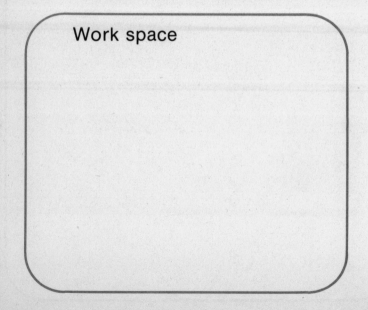

Work space

It has rained on 36 of the last 90 days. What percentage of the 90 days was it raining?

_____

In our city elections, 40% of the people voted for George Evans and 39% voted for Barbara Davis. What percentage did not vote?

Step 1.   Find out the percentage of people who voted.

Step 2.   Subtract the percentage who voted from all who could have voted.

Answer _____

On Saturday, 21% of my friends went skating and 46% went to the movies. The rest went to a football game. What percentage went to the game?

Answer _____

Work space

Lee moved 60% of the chairs in the cafeteria. There were 450 chairs. How many chairs were not moved?

Step 1.   Find out the percentage of chairs not moved.

Step 2.   Multiply percentage not moved by the number of chairs.

Answer _____

Of the 350 people at the movie, 2% left before it was over. How many people stayed for the whole movie?

Answer _____

Work space

In a building, 96% of the apartments were rented. There were 350 apartments. How many apartments were not rented?

Work space

A local department store has 200 employees. If 65% of them walk to work, how many do not walk to work?

Work space

Kate gets $6.20 a week for her paper route. She spends 60% on food, 10% on clothes, and saves the rest. How much money does she save?

_____

Teresa needs $8.50 to buy a blouse. She earns 70% by babysitting and 10% by washing her father's car. She earns the rest by cleaning her room. How much money does she earn by cleaning her room?

_____

Work space

A new car costs $9400. Each of the 4 tires on the car is worth 1% of the cost of the car. What are all 4 of the tires worth together?

_____

Rachel needed some money to buy a sewing machine. Her parents *each* gave her 10% of the cost of the machine. The machine cost $525.00. How much money did Rachel's parents give her?

_____

A meal at a restaurant cost $64.00. Sally paid 24% of the bill, Harry 21%, Beth 27% and Alex paid the rest. How much did Alex pay?

_____

Three friends needed to save $48.00 for a weekend trip. Carol saved 32% and Nan saved 18%. Lynn saved the rest. How much did Lynn save?

_____

Work space

Reminder page: time

30 minutes = $\frac{1}{2}$ hour   60 minutes = 1 hour

What time is it?

_____   _____   _____

Draw in the clock hands to show:

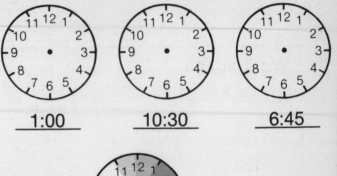

1:00   10:30   6:45

Start at 9:00 A.M. What time will it be 2 hours later?

_____

Start at 11:00 A.M. What time will it be 3 hours later?

_____

Bert started to work at 8:00 A.M. He had been at work $3\frac{1}{2}$ hours when he finished. What time was it?

_____

Paula went to work at midnight. She worked 4 hours and had a 1 hour break, worked 3 more hours and went home. What time did she go home?

_____

Work space

At 8:00 A.M. the plane left Omaha. It was in the air for 45 minutes and landed in Davenport. It was on the ground 15 minutes. It arrived in New York 3 hours later. What time did it arrive in New York?

_____

Steve took the bus from Chicago to Green Bay. The bus left Chicago at 10:00 A.M. 1 hour and 45 minutes later it arrived in Milwaukee. It stopped there for 15 minutes, then went to Green Bay. It arrived in Green Bay $2\frac{1}{2}$ hours later. What time did the bus arrive in Green Bay?

_____

Work space

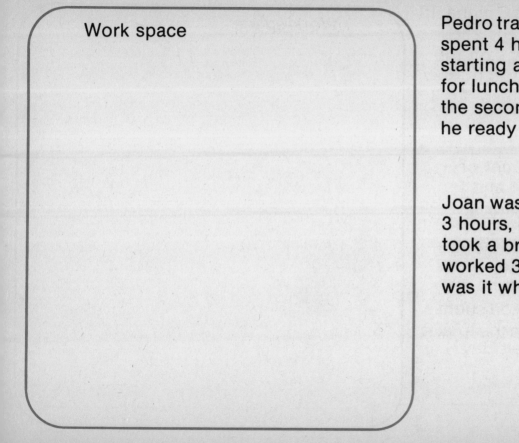

Work space

Pedro trained dogs. On Monday he spent 4 hours with the first group starting at 8:00 A.M. After an hour for lunch he worked 3 hours with the second group. What time was he ready to go home?

_____

Joan was a doctor. She worked for 3 hours, starting at 7:00 A.M. She took a break for $\frac{1}{2}$ hour and then worked $3\frac{1}{2}$ more hours. What time was it when she finished?

_____

On Monday you left on your vacation at 11:00 A.M. You stopped for lunch for 1 hour and spent 1 hour shopping. You arrived in Detroit at 6:00 P.M. How much time had you spent driving?

Step 1.   Find the total amount of time between when you left and when you arrived.

Step 2.   Find the amount of time you spent for lunch and shopping.

Step 3.   Subtract the time you spent for lunch and shopping from the total time.

Answer _____

Work space

Margaret earned $5.00 an hour. One day she worked from 8:00 A.M. to 10:00 A.M., from 11:00 to 12:00 Noon, and from 3:00 P.M. to 5:00 P.M. How much money did she earn that day?

Step 1.   Find out how many hours Margaret worked that day.

Step 2.   Multiply the number of hours she worked by her hourly rate.

Answer _____

Work space

Cost of electricity

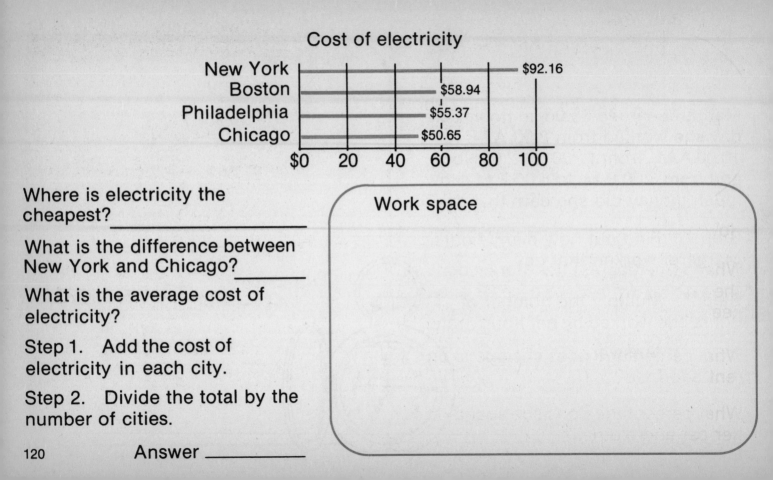

New York — $92.16
Boston — $58.94
Philadelphia — $55.37
Chicago — $50.65

$0   20   40   60   80   100

Where is electricity the cheapest? _____

What is the difference between New York and Chicago? _____

What is the average cost of electricity?

Step 1.   Add the cost of electricity in each city.

Step 2.   Divide the total by the number of cities.

120   Answer _____

Work space

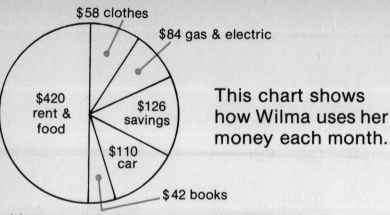

$58 clothes

$84 gas & electric

$420 rent & food

$126 savings

$110 car

$42 books

This chart shows how Wilma uses her money each month.

How much does she use altogether? _____

What percentage of her money does she save? (Turn back to page 89 if you need a hint.) _____

What percentage does she spend on rent and food? _____

What percentage does she spend on her car and clothes? _____

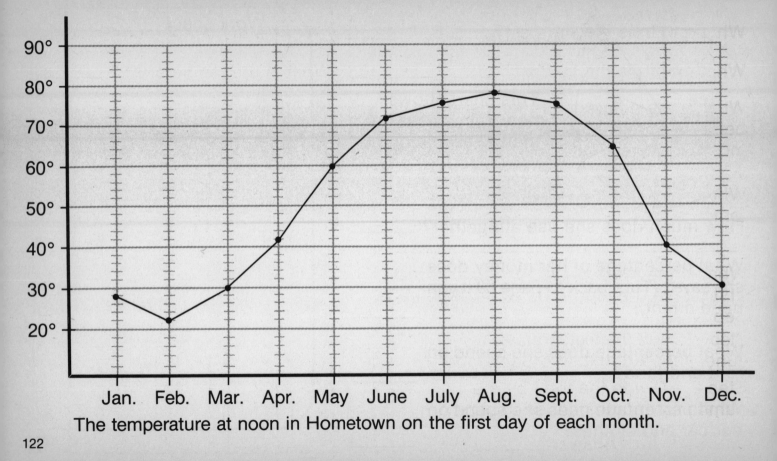

The temperature at noon in Hometown on the first day of each month.

What month is the warmest? _____ What is the temperature? _____

What month is the coldest? _____ What is the temperature? _____

What is the difference in temperature between the warmest and coldest month?
_____

What two months have the same temperature?

_____

What is the average temperature on the first day of the month between June and September?

Step 1.   Add the temperatures for June, July, August, and September.

Step 2.   Divide the total by the number of months added together.

Answer _____

Work space

123

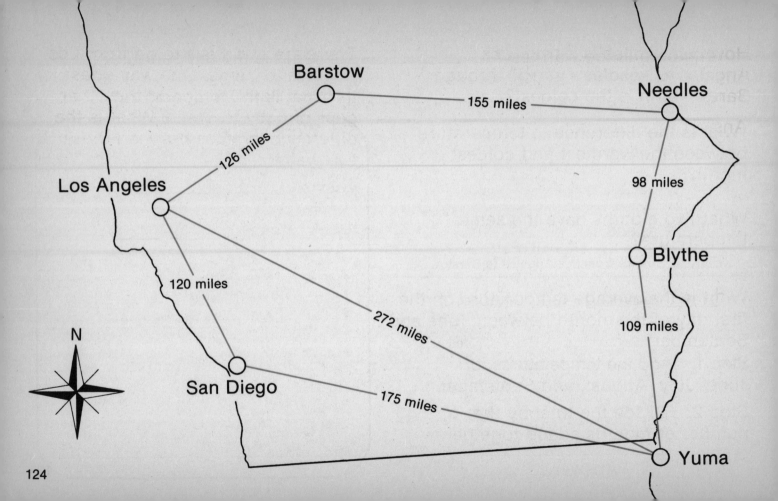

Barstow

Needles

155 miles

126 miles

98 miles

Los Angeles

Blythe

120 miles

272 miles

109 miles

N

San Diego

175 miles

Yuma

124

How many miles is it from Los Angeles to Needles if you go through Barstow?

Answer _____

Work space

_____ miles from Los Angeles to Barstow

+ _____ miles from Barstow to Needles

_____ miles from Los Angeles to Needles

There are two ways to go from Los Angeles to Yuma. One way goes through San Diego, and the other goes directly to Yuma. What is the difference in miles between these two ways?

Answer _____

Work space

Use the map on page 124 for the following questions.

If you drive at 40 miles per hour from San Diego to Los Angeles, how long will it take? _____

What is the distance from Needles to Yuma, traveling through Blythe?

_____

If you leave Needles at 3:00 P.M. and travel at 55 miles per hour, how many miles will you cover by 5:00 P.M.?

_____

How much further will you have to go? _____

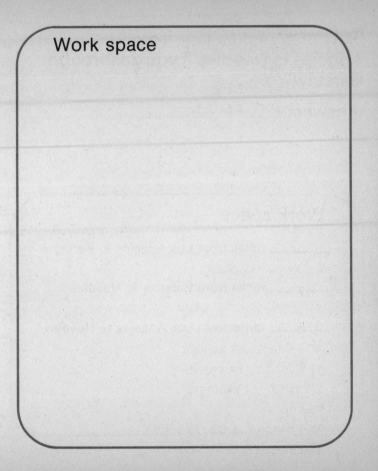

Work space

Answers

4 90 stamps

5 19 sticks   18 pets

6 13 pencils   4 people

7 35 children

8 1620 people   1203 people

9 15 animals   9 animals   24 animals

10 11 buildings   20 buildings   26 buildings
    46 buildings

11 66 shells

12 3 comics

13 6 friends   12 plants

14 12 pages   25 years

15 29 people

16 22 coins   21 years older

17 37 apples   146 games

18 17 cookies   74 years

19 27 miles   41 kilometers

20 288 books

21 336 ounces   1,000 milliliters

22 180 pieces   276 pieces

23 192 miles   288 miles   240 kilo
    420 kilometers

24 4,000 meters   16,000 meters

25 32 rows   640 plants

26 324 windows   1,296 pieces of

27 780 tables   364 chairs

28 5 desks

29 4 gallons   8 quarts   2 liters

30 28 students   7 students

31 148 cars   45 liters

32 30 liters   20 gallons

33 19 papers   17 papers

34 57 students   551 students

35 97 storms   1261 storms

36 4 people

37 450 pounds   180 kilograms

38 16 colors   19 colors

39 663 kilometers   285 miles

40 200 cars per hour

41 120 pages

62   ⅘ loaf   5/3 or 1⅔ bowls
63   7/2 or 3½ grams   3/2 or 1½ pounds
64   ⅚ hour
65   3/2 or 1½ days   2,905 books
66   45 square feet   21 square meters
67   125 people   2,700 raisins
68   78 kph   18¾ hours
69    $1.94
70    $14.65 $6.81
71    $690.00 $760.00
72    $514.00 $242.90
73    $1.75 $2.05
74    $17.70 $12.50
75    $137.00 $127.40
76    $7841.00 $1167.00
77    $.84 $3.60
78    $1.35 $40.80 $57.00
79    $16.80 $10.50
80    $32.64 $11.75